ONE BANANA
A JUNGLE COUNTING BOOK

by Amy Noonus
illustrated by Pat Stewart

GT
PUBLISHING
New York

Text copyright © 1997 GT Publishing Corporation.
Illustrations copyright © 1997 Pat Stewart.
All rights reserved.
No part of this book may be used or reproduced in any manner
whatsoever without written permission from the publisher.
For information address GT Publishing Corporation,
16 East 40th Street, New York, New York 10016.

One banana lies on the jungle floor.

Two hungry monkeys want one tasty banana.

**Three leaping leopards
chase two hungry monkeys.**

**Four bright birds distract
three leaping leopards.**

**Five busy flies buzz past
four bright birds.**

**Six swishing tails brush away
five buzzing flies.**

**Seven bouncy baboons watch
six swishing tails.**

Eight enormous elephants carry seven bouncy baboons.

9

Nine pretty flowers attract
eight enormous elephants.

Ten tiny ants see nine pretty flowers.

Ten terrified ants scurry in a hurry.

Nine pretty flowers shadow ten fleeing ants.

**Eight enormous elephants pick
nine pretty flowers.**

Seven bouncy baboons urge eight enormous elephants onward.

**Six swishing tails wave
seven bouncy baboons on their way.**

Five quick flies dodge six swishing tails.

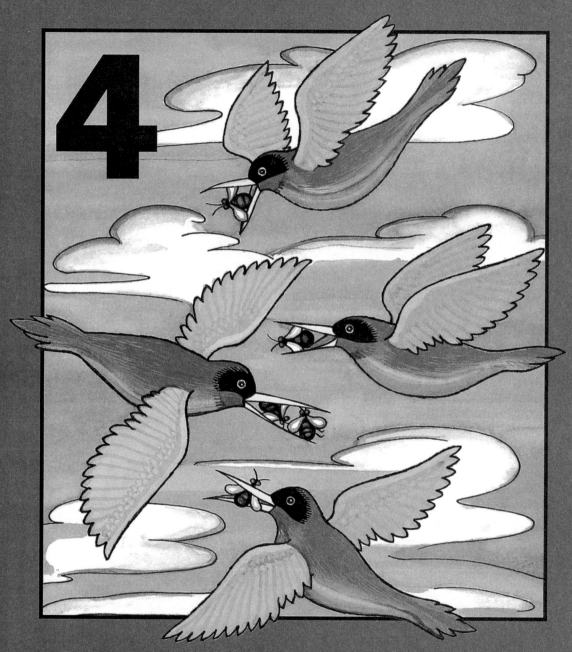

**Four bright birds swallow
five tasty flies.**

**Three leaping leopards ignore
four flying birds.**

Two clever monkeys hide from three frustrated leopards.

**One tasty banana is shared by
two hungry monkeys.**

One banana peel lies on the jungle floor.

1

2

3

4

5

6

7

8

9

10

MY ALPHABET LUNCH

by **Amy Noonus**

illustrated by
Erik Doescher

GT

PUBLISHING
New York

I like an Apple in my lunch,

Bananas are good, too.

Some **C**hocolate **C**ola hits the spot,

and **D**oughnuts—just a few.

But even more, I like an **E**gg

with **F**rench **F**ries, **F**ruit, and **F**ish,

Some **G**rapes with **G**orgonzola and

a **H**am and **H**erring dish.

Ice cream's good with **J**elly

if you add some **K**ale and toss.

And **L**icorice **L**asagna's best

with **M**ustard-**M**ango sauce.

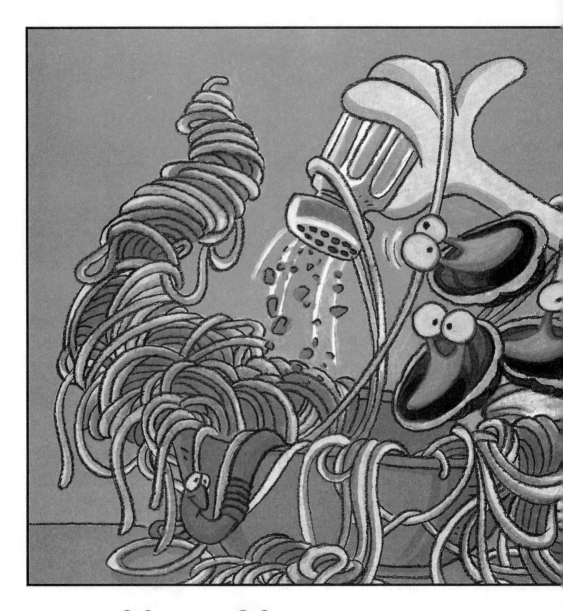

Some **N**utmeg **N**oodles would be nice

with **O**ysters on the shell,

But without Parsley Pancakes

I'd feel **Q**ueasy and unwell.

Raspberry **R**avioli,

Scallop **S**andwich, **S**ugar **S**oup.

A **T**apioca **T**aco

Under **V**eal and **W**alnut goop.

If you **X**-rayed my whole stomach, I'm sure

that **Y**ou would see, I eat a bit of everything

—from **A** to **Z**ucchini!